Start Pianojazz

MIKE CORNICK

UNIVERSAL EDITION

ISMN M-008-05895-0

Start Pianojazz

Start Pianojazz has been written to answer the needs of the pianist who wants to play jazz, or at least jazzy-styled pieces, at a fairly early stage in their learning. From the teacher's point of view, the problem has often been to find pieces which pose the minimum of technical difficulty while managing to retain the appropriate stylistic elements. It is to be hoped that among the ballads, the blues, the jazz–waltz and the medium and up-tempo swing or on-beat pieces included in this book, there will be something for everyone.

Each piece has a facing page of notes which provide some hints on style, form and rhythm as well as a few practice strategies. Of the various elements which, together, give rise to a recognisable musical style, it is usually, in my experience, the question of rhythm which causes the greatest difficulty in playing jazzy-styled pieces. For this reason, explanation of the application of the "swing" quaver symbol has been constantly reiterated; once the principle is fully understood, however, subsequent explanations may be happily disregarded.

Chord symbols have been provided where it has been thought appropriate and these may be of use to some pupils and also to teachers who like to improvise a *secondo* part on another piano/keyboard or even on the same instrument, having moved the pupil's performance up an octave as necessary. The following points should, however, be noted:

- The chord symbols will not always take account of every note in the chord or each movement in the harmony. Neither will they necessarily indicate a bass note which is not the root of the chord.

- In circumstances where the written harmony is deliberately sparse, chord symbols may indicate an implied harmony which goes beyond the notation of the piece.

Although no fully written "solos" have been included in this volume, the accompanying notes for some of the pieces contain suggestions which may encourage pupils to free themselves from the notation to a greater or lesser extent. It is this willingness to "let go" of the printed page and to begin to create variation, rhythmically, melodically and harmonically which marks the beginning of playing real jazz and this should be actively encouraged. Subsequent books in this series will offer jazz-styled solos for each piece as well as providing players with a helping hand in constructing their own improvisations.

Finally, I would like to thank those of my pupils who played the first drafts of these pieces and who, in doing so, helped to focus my attention on the strengths and weaknesses of those initial ideas. This book is dedicated to them in recognition of their enthusiasm, interest and encouragement.

Mike Cornick
September, 1997

Contents

Form and Style

A Minor Waltz is built on a four note bass line which descends under a sustained tonic:

Note how this idea is modified, first with a suspension in the dominant chord (bar 8) and, finally, by passing through an F-natural before arriving at its delayed final cadence.

Rhythm

Note the presence of the "swing" quavers symbol at the head of the page:

This symbol instructs us to play *all* quaver movement with a triplet rhythm. Applying this to the first four bars of melody, we should now play:

It is important to understand and to be able to apply the "swing" quavers instruction because this is an essential rhythmic feature of a great deal of jazz. The use of the symbol avoids the sort of complicated notation shown above and allows the player to apply the rhythmic "swing" as a matter of interpretation.

Practice

- It is a good idea to learn and practise the left hand of this piece first since it moves entirely in dotted minims, minims and crotchets.

- Having established a secure left hand accompaniment, learn and practise the right hand melody, noting that it begins on the second beat of the bar. The first two crotchets of the melody, therefore, are un-accented: the first accented melody note is the first quaver of bar 2.

- When playing both right and left hand parts together, try to ensure that the strict rhythmic progression of the left hand is not disturbed by the syncopations of the melody.

- Aim for a relaxed performance speed of about ♩ = 130, observing dynamic markings, phrasing, slurs, and staccatos.

- Finally, as a step towards building your own improvisations, feel free to experiment by developing variations on the melody. Why not begin by thinking in terms of partly inverting the melodic line?

A Minor Waltz

MIKE CORNICK

UE 17361 L

Form and Style

The City Sleeps is a jazz ballad which is built on a two-bar left hand figure which moves in minims:

Notice how this repeated phrase continues throughout the piece except for the last four bars.

The melody is derived from the *blues scale*, starting on A, rather than from the scale of A minor.

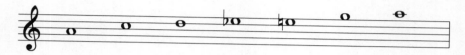

…and this explains:
- the absence of G-sharps (which you might expect as the sharpened leading-note of A minor)
- the frequent occurrence of the flattened 5th of the A minor scale – E-flat.

Rhythm

As in *A Minor Waltz*, the quavers should "swing" and we should remember that this applies to *all* quaver movement, even when one of the quavers is tied to another note:

Take care to ensure that the anticipations are played correctly: e.g. notice how the accented E-flat is played on the last (swing) quaver of the bar:

Practice

- Begin by practising the repeated left hand figure. Use the suggested fingering or a suitable alternative in order to achieve a controlled, quiet and *legato* (smooth) two-bar phrase.

- Remember that the left hand is an accompaniment and that it should never be allowed to overpower the melody. Practise until the left hand part is secure.

- Learn and practise the right hand melody using the suggested fingering or a suitable alternative in order to produce an appropriate *legato*. Make sure that this part is also secure before attempting to play right and left hand parts together.

- Finally, try to observe the dynamic markings, staccatos, and particularly the accenting of most of the E-flats.

The City Sleeps

MIKE CORNICK

Form and Style

Just Walkin'… introduces the idea of the "walking bass". This is a term which describes a jazz bass line which moves, usually by step, in regular note values. This walking bass consists of the first four notes of the descending A minor (melodic) scale in minims, forming a two-bar phrase:

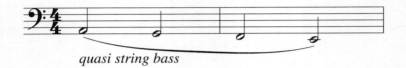

quasi string bass

The Italian term *quasi* means: as if or resembling.
Quasi string bass, therefore, means: resembling a string (or double) bass.

This 16-bar piece evolves from the first two-bar phrase which is modified or repeated (either at pitch or an octave higher) throughout.

Rhythm

Once again, the "swing" quavers indication is present and, as always, we must remember that this refers to rests, tied quavers and syncopations:

Practice

- Once again, practise the left hand first, repeating the "walking bass" figure with the sound of the string bass in mind; sustain the minims to produce an effective *legato* but make a clear attack on each note to imitate the effect of the *pizzicato* bass playing.

- Practise the right hand melody separately. Because the notes of the melody can be played without any change of hand position, you will be able to concentrate on accuracy in pitch and rhythm and will, at a later stage, be able to give some attention to phrasing and articulation.

  N.B. The small line over or under a notehead:

  …indicates *tenuto*, which means that the note is held for its full value…or even, perhaps, for a little longer. It also suggests a slight emphasis or accenting of the note.

- When playing right and left hands together, try not to allow the syncopations and anticipations of the melody to distort the regularity of the walking bass line.

- Finally, build up the dynamic level through each two-bar phrase from *mezzo-piano* (moderately soft) to *mezzo-forte* (moderately loud) or *forte* (loud) as indicated.

Just Walkin'...

MIKE CORNICK

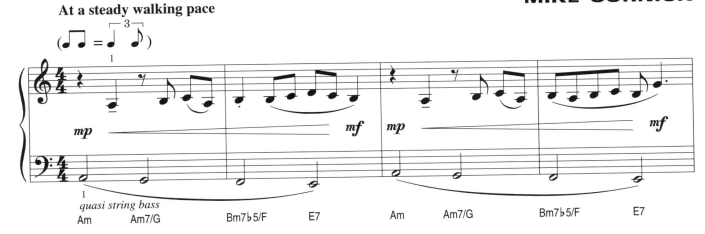

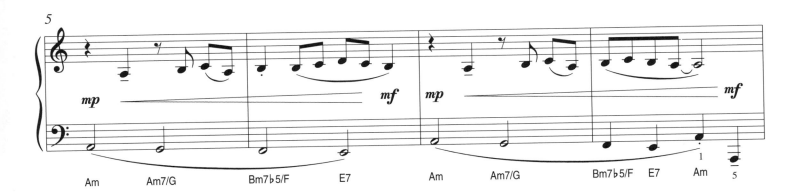

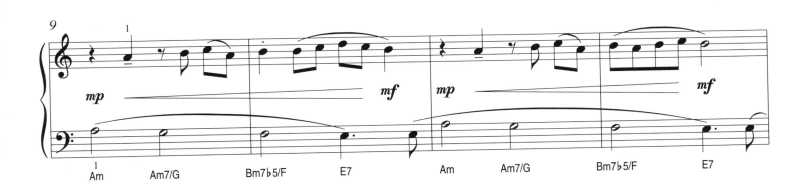

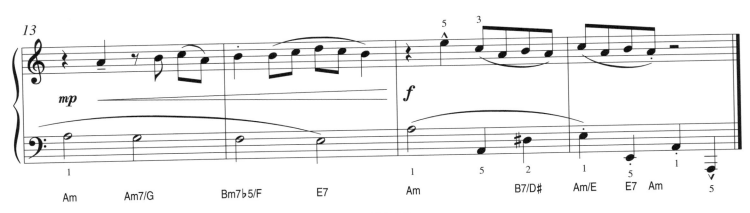

UE 17361 L

Form and Style

Another Dawn is a jazz ballad which, like much contemporary jazz, borrows freely from the Western European "Classical" tradition. Consequently, it is the shifting and ambiguous chromatic harmonies, rather than the rhythmic elements, which relate the piece to jazz.

Rhythm

Melody and harmony progress mainly in crotchets and minims and, in the absence of the "swing" quavers symbol, all quavers are to be played evenly.

Practice

- Learn and practise the melodic line, adopting a fingering which facilitates the phrasing.

- Again, in practising the left hand, use the given fingering or a suitable alternative which will permit an easy *legato* transition from one chord to the next.

  N.B.   *sempre*   =   always
            legato   =   smooth

- Aim for a performance tempo of about ♩ = 90.

- Try to observe the indicated dynamics or devise your own to enhance the effect of the piece.

- As you gain in confidence, why not experiment with creating variation in the melodic line and, subsequently, perhaps, in the harmony as the first step towards the improvisation of a jazz solo?

e.g. at bar 13:

might develop into:

and then into:

Another Dawn

Slowly and thoughtfully
(in even quavers)

MIKE CORNICK

Form and Style

Clowning Around is a "swing" styled two-part invention in which the two "voices" only play together on three brief occasions. Consequently, no chord symbols have been included.

The two "voices" might be thought of as different instruments…a trumpet and a trombone, for instance. The lower voice plays the very simple idea:

 and receives the answer:  and so on.

Rhythm

The "swing" quaver symbol is present and there are a great number of quavers to swing! As always take care with:

 and

Practice

- This is a piece for which separate hand practice may not be very helpful. Because left and right hands "answer" one another, try to learn both parts simultaneously.

- Having securely established notes and rhythm, work towards a performance tempo of about ♩ = 135 (or faster!). Try to take note of the details, like staccato marks, accents and slurs.

  N.B.   *sfz*   =   *sforzando* (Italian) =   accented or forced

- When you have reached performance standard, complete with dynamics of course, then be prepared to experiment. Try the effect of a *forte* right hand part and a *mezzo-piano* left hand…or, perhaps, the other way around!

Clowning Around

MIKE CORNICK

Form and Style

Bassman Blues is a twelve-bar blues in G major which is built on a walking bass line derived from the notes of the tonic, sub-dominant and dominant chords. Thus:

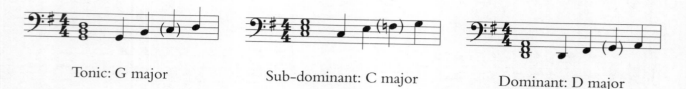

Tonic: G major   Sub-dominant: C major   Dominant: D major

The melody consits of repetitions, variations and transpositions of the *riff*:

A *riff* is a short repeated jazz phrase which, with small variations, will fit the changing harmony.

Rhythm

Note the presence of the "swing" quaver symbol once again; take care with such rhythms as:

Practice

- As with other pieces in the book which are constructed on a "walking" bass line, learn, practise and secure the left hand part first.

- When the bass line is secure, practise the changing *riffs* until you feel confident enough to combine the parts.

- Once again, try not to allow the strict time of the bass line to be disrupted by the syncopations of the right hand part.

- Take careful note of phrasing, accents, staccato marks and dynamics, aiming for a performance tempo of about ♩ = 125.

- Finally, why not experiment by substituting a new *riff* of your own? How can you modify, extend and transpose this *riff* in order to accomodate the changing harmony?

Bassman Blues

MIKE CORNICK

At a walking bass tempo

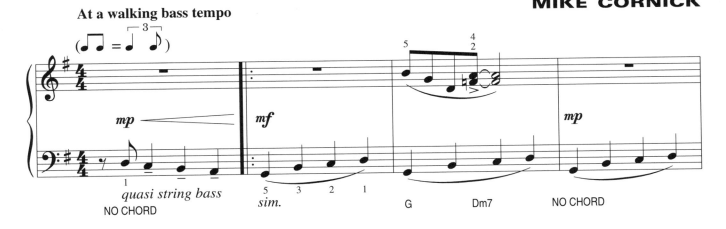

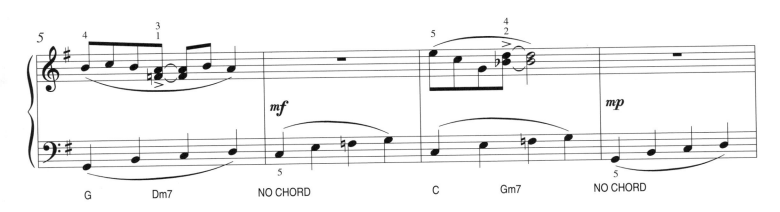

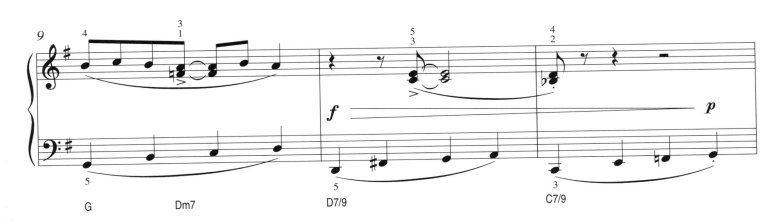

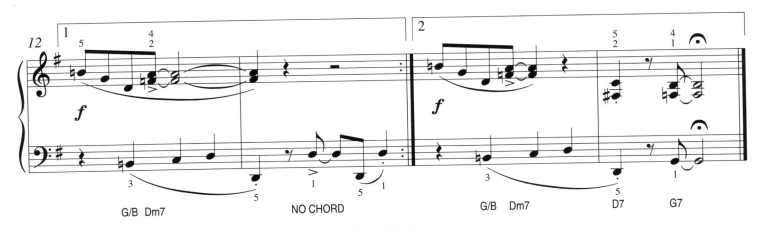

UE 17361 L

Form and Style

Mellow Fellow is a medium tempo "swing" piece which grows from a melodic idea stated in the first three bars of the piece. Note the changing sound of the tonic chord (F) as it passes from root position (the 3rd of the chord, A, is in the melodic line) to F6, Fmaj7 and then back again by the same route to the root position triad.

The piece includes a number of very small notes (printed in "cue" sized notation): ♪ . This very short time value note, usually referred to as a *grace* note (and which is technically known as an *acciaccatura*), is played so that it has the shortest possible duration. Many jazz pianists make use of the grace note in an attempt to imitate the effect of other instruments which are capable of pitch "bending".

Rhythm

Note the presence of the "swing" quaver symbol and interpret the quaver movement accordingly.

Note that: and

are simply alternative notations and should be interpreted, when the "swing" quaver symbol is present, as:

Practice

● Learn and practise the left and right hand parts of the piece separately, taking care of the syncopations in the melodic line when these parts are combined.

● Once the piece is secure and the details of articulation attended to, consider how the melody line of the first three bars is constructed. All the melody notes (except the final quaver) are drawn from the tonic chord of F major: F, A and C.

● Why not experiment by substituting your own melodic line, drawing your notes from the chords in the same way?

For example:

Mellow Fellow

MIKE CORNICK

Form and Style

The Scat Rat is another twelve-bar blues with a long three-bar riff drawn from the blues scale on D:

The blues scale: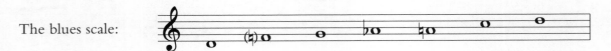

The Scat Rat riff:

Although it may not be immediately apparent because of the inversions of the chords used and the "added" notes which arise when these chords combine with the melody, the basic chord progression is very orthodox:

i.e.

	Tonic		Subdominant		Tonic – Subdominant		Tonic – Subdominant – Tonic	
	Subdominant		Subdominant		Tonic – Subdominant		Tonic – Subdominant – Tonic	
	Dominant		Subdominant		Tonic		Dominant	

or, to end: | Tonic – Subdominant – Tonic ‖

Rhythm

Note the presence of the "swing" quaver symbol.

Practice

- Once again, learn and practise the left hand chords until they can provide a secure accompaniment for the melody.

- It may help, in working on the phrasing of this part, to imagine the left hand chords as representing a section of instruments in a big jazz band…perhaps the saxophones.

- Learn and practise the melodic riff until it is secure before combining right and left hands. Aim to build the dynamic of each playing of the three-bar riff from *piano* (***p*** = *piano* = soft) to *forte* (***f*** = *forte* = loud) as indicated.

- When the piece is secure and you have achieved an appropriate performance speed (perhaps as fast as ♩ = 160 or more!), consider the possibility of substituting your own riff. Take the notes of your riff directly from the chords:

  i.e. D7   Bar 1: select from D, F-sharp, A and C
  G7/9   Bar 2: select from G, B, D, F and A

  or simply think in terms of the (D) blues scale.

The Scat Rat

MIKE CORNICK

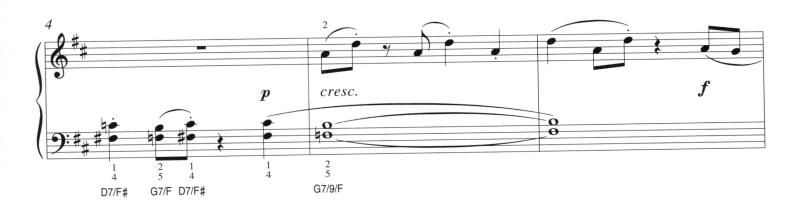

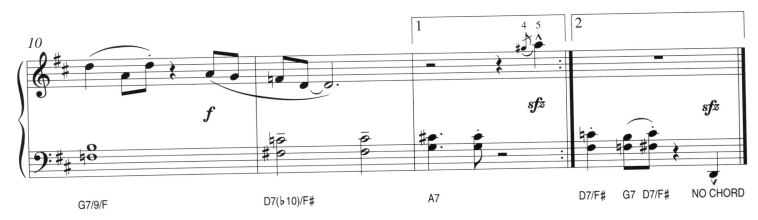

Form and Style

Latin-Eights is a bossa nova–styled piece which is based on the chord of the (added) seventh (major or minor). The chord is divided so that the left hand plays a sequence of rising fifths whilst the right hand moves in parallel in intervals of a fourth:

Rhythm

The piece must be played in strict time *in even quavers* to gain its effect and it may be helpful, initially, to think of the bar as consisting of eight quavers accented to produce the rhythm:

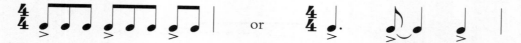

Practice

- Begin by learning the rising sequence of chords shown above, and then add the repeated off-beat accented fifth of the chord: finally, complete the phrase. e.g.:

- Use the fingering shown (or a suitable alternative) so that each one-bar phrase falls comfortably under your hands.

- Bars 9–12 may present some difficulties because the added seventh chords are no longer always moving by step. Again, give careful consideration to the adoption of a fingering which allows for the comfortable transition from one chord position to the next and which also permits the indicated slurring of the *appoggiaturas* (which are dissonant notes in chords which resolve, usually on a weaker beat in the bar).

- Finally, try to observe the indicated dynamics so that there is a *crescendo* through bars 1–4, 5–8 and 9–12, followed by the immediate reduction to *mezzo-piano* on the last beat of bar 12 (the Italian term *subito* means suddenly) and a return to **mf** in bar 16 of the first time bar and bar 15 of the second time bar.

Latin-Eights

At a steady bossa-nova tempo
(in even quavers)

MIKE CORNICK

Form and Style

Definitely Blue is, once again, substantially derived from the blues scale on D:

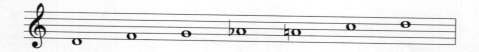

The left hand plays a descending four note "walking bass" figure whilst the melody imitates a solo instrument…imagine, perhaps, a muted trumpet. Once again, the *acciaccatura* (♪) is used as the pianist's best equivalent to playing a note which falls between the available pitches of the piano keys but which, of course, can easily be produced on a brass or woodwind instrument.

Rhythm

Note the presence of the "swing" quaver symbol.

In general, play the quavers which fall behind the beat later rather than earlier in order to produce the appropriate relaxed "bluesy" feel whilst ensuring that "on beat" notes remain strictly on the beat.

Practice

- Build the melody on a well practised and secure bass line, making clear the distinction between:

  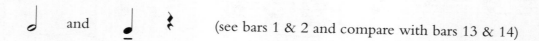 (see bars 1 & 2 and compare with bars 13 & 14)

- In playing the melody, take account of the *slurs* and the *staccato* marks, ensuring that the rests are observed in such phrases as:

- Except in the chordal passages, try to aim for an appropriate balance between left and right hands so that the melody is clearly heard over the bass line.

- Finally, add some light and shade to the performance by observing the dynamic markings.

Definitely Blue

MIKE CORNICK

UE 17361 L

Form and Style

Time Passes is a medium tempo "swing" piece which develops from the *motif*:

N.B. A *motif* is a short musical figure or idea which forms the basis of much which is to follow in a piece of music.

This *motif*, in its travels, explores the A-minor scale as it passes through *tonic* (A-minor), *sub-dominant* (D minor) and *dominant* (E major) harmony.

Rhythm

Remember, once again, to interpret all quaver movement in accordance with the "swing" quaver symbol and, as always, take care to think about how this affects tied quavers.

e.g.

Practice

- Once the notes and rhythm of the left and right hand parts are secure and confidently combined, give particular attention to the finer details such as slurs and staccatos. e.g.

Right hand, bars 1–6: 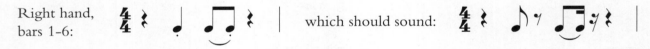 which should sound:

- In the "middle eight" (i.e. bars 9–16), pay particular attention to notes occurring on the last "swing" quaver of the bar, delaying them appropriately, as follows:

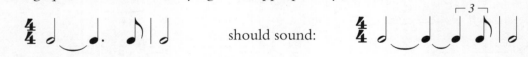 should sound:

- Finally, once the piece can be confidently performed (ideally at a tempo of ♩ = 120, which measures the passing time at two crotchet beats per second), why not give some thought to substituting your own *motif* in the first eight bars of the piece?

- Perhaps begin with a simple version of the existing motif, transposing and developing the idea, bar by bar, to accord with the simple harmonic progression, as follows:
  tonic – sub-dominant – tonic – dominant. e.g.

Time Passes

MIKE CORNICK

Form and Style

Mister Marcus is a blues-styled "on-beat" piece written in alternating bars of $\frac{3}{4}$ and $\frac{4}{4}$. Effectively, at a performance tempo of ♩ = 165 (or faster), the piece sounds as if it has a $\frac{7}{4}$ or $\frac{7}{8}$ time signature, but the shorter bars make it easier to read.

Aim for strict time in a heavily accented style.

Rhythm

Although apparently quite complicated in its appearance when shared between left and right hands, the rhythm of the $\frac{3}{4}$ bars is simply heard as:

and the alternating roles of left and right hands should soon be grasped.

Practice

● It may be helpful to begin practising the co-ordination of right and left hands in the opening rhythm of the piece *away* from the keyboard with hands on a table top or the closed lid of the piano:

Right Hand:

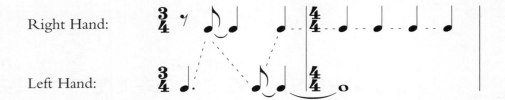

Left Hand:

or simply to play the rhythm on two C's before strarting work on the actual piece:

● The given fingering provides a great deal of work for the fourth and fifth fingers of the right hand and alternative possibilities may well suggest themselves. It may be worth bearing in mind the advantages of a pattern of fingering which can be transposed to the sub-dominant and dominant positions of the $\frac{4}{4}$ bar motif and which will accommodate its slight variations.

Mister Marcus

MIKE CORNICK

UE 17361 L

LX/01

OTHER TITLES FOR THE PIANO

by MIKE CORNICK

UE 16550	**Easy Jazzy Piano**
UE 16590	**Easy Jazzy Piano 2**
UE 16577	**Easy Jazzy Duets - Piano**
UE 19756	**Jazzy Duets - Piano 1**
UE 16536	**Jazzy Duets - Piano 2**
UE 19762	**Blue Piano**
UE 14050	**Jazz Improvisation for Piano and Keyboard** *including CD*
UE 30413	**Mike Cornick's Piano Ragtime**
UE 16591	**Mike Cornick's Piano Ragtime Duets**
UE 16592	**Mike Cornick's Boogie Piano Book**

Universal Edition

SHOWROOM:
48 Great Marlborough Street
London W1V 2BN
FREEfone: 0800 525 566
FREEfax: 0800 525 567

SALES DEPT:
38 Eldon Way, Paddock Wood
Kent TN12 6BE
Telephone: 01892 833422